Glorious
Guides

PROPHET ADAM AS
Activity Book

Writers

Maria Reza
Junaid Bilal

Illustrator

Dur e Haya Hina

The following icons have been used in this Activity Book.

 What you need   Note for grown-ups

 What you do   Top tips

 Game Set-up

(جَزَاكَ اللهُ اخيرًا كَثِيرٌ)

May Allah SWT accept and reward all who have contributed to this project.
Special thanks to Abu-Saalihah Bin Ayyub for help, guidance and motivation.

Glorious Guides - Stories of the Prophets is part of the *Lasting Legacy* initiative, aimed at Muslim kids everywhere. A legacy for our children and our future.

First Edition 2018
Second Edition 2019

Published by Wisdom Publications
www.wisdompublications.co.uk

ISBN 978-1-911314-76-9

Illustrations by Dur e Haya Hina

www.lastinglegacy.club

بِسْمِ اللهِ الرَّحْمٰنِ الرَّحِيمِ

Bismillah hir rahman nir raheem

In the name of Allah, the most Gracious, the most Merciful.

This Bountiful Book belongs to Brilliant and Brainy

_____

Table of Contents

Benefits of using games & activities with the Storybook

Read to learn – As part of their education, children need to not only demonstrate that they can read, but also show an ability to process text, understand meaning, and integrate what they learn with what they already know. This makes **Reading Comprehension** extremely important while reading any type of text.

Incorporating **interactive games and activities** with reading gives children an opportunity to:
➡ practice and strengthen their reading comprehension skills.
➡ recall and analyse what they have read.
➡ apply critical thinking skills and deductive reasoning, and demonstrate logical inference and understanding of scope.

Learning while reading, and having fun in the process, is surely a win, win situation.

Using this Activity Book alongside the Storybook can be pivotal to achieving one of the main aims of the "Glorious Guides" series: to see how Qur'anic stories are applicable to our own lives and how we can gain guidance from them.

Recommended Use

This Activity Book is designed to be used alongside the Storybook of Prophet Adam AS.

➡ All activities should be done under adult supervision.

➡ Only one or two activities should be done at a time. This book is not designed to be completed in one go.

➡ Activities can be done in any order and as many times as desired.

➡ Activities are pitched at various difficulty levels; you can select the ones better suited to your child's age range.

➡ Some quiet time should be selected to do the activities, keeping disruptions to the minimum.

➡ Adults should encourage discussion and focus on the learning of key concepts.

➡ Repetition is key, little and often.

➡ Remember to provide lots of praise and have fun.

Once the Activity Book has been completed, fill out the certificate provided at the end and present it to your child.

It is as easy as 1, 2, 3

We have read the Dua of Prophet Adam AS in the story. Let's practice reading it a bit more.

 ## What you need:
–Activity Sheet
–Colouring pens

What you do:
– Read the Dua once and then colour-in the 1st star.
– Read the Dua again and colour-in the 2nd star.
– Now read the Dua one last time, just to make sure you are really good at reading it, and colour-in the 3rd star.

Note for grown-ups: Encouraging children to memorise the Dua of Prophet Adam AS is a great idea because they are then more likely to offer this dua frequently. This Dua earned Allah SWT's forgiveness for Prophet Adam AS so surely it can earn us all forgiveness, too. InshAllah.

For younger children, who find it hard to memorise this dua, a small and simple "Astaghfirullah" can be a good start.

For older children, make it more challenging. Instead of colouring they have to put three grains of rice into each star. Picking up the rice, one by one, with their thumb and little finger (not using middle three fingers). This will be a good way of excercising fine motor skills, and add a fun twist as well.

رَبَّنَا ظَلَمْنَا أَنْفُسَنَا

وَإِنْ لَّمْ تَغْفِرْ لَنَا وَتَرْحَمْنَا

لَنَكُونَنَّ مِنَ الْخَاسِرِينَ

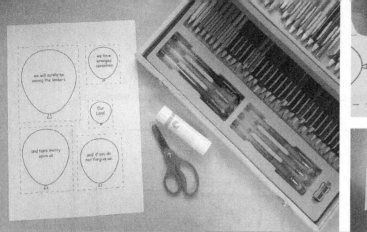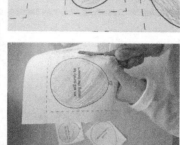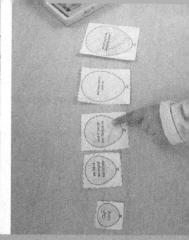

Sorting by size

Now that you can read the Dua of Prophet Adam AS, let's see if you remember its meaning.

 ## What you need:
−Activity Sheet
−Colouring pens
−Child−safe scissors

 ## What you do:
−Take Activity sheet and colour−in all the balloons.
−Once you are happy with your colouring, cut along the dotted lines as neatly as you can.
−Arrange the balloons from smallest to biggest, to complete the Dua of Prophet Adam AS.
−Now read it out loud to make sure everything is in the right order.

Note for grown-ups: In addition to memorising the Arabic text of this dua, it is very important to know its meaning and understand it.
This activity is a fun way to revise the meaning and also involves scissor−use skills and concept of size.

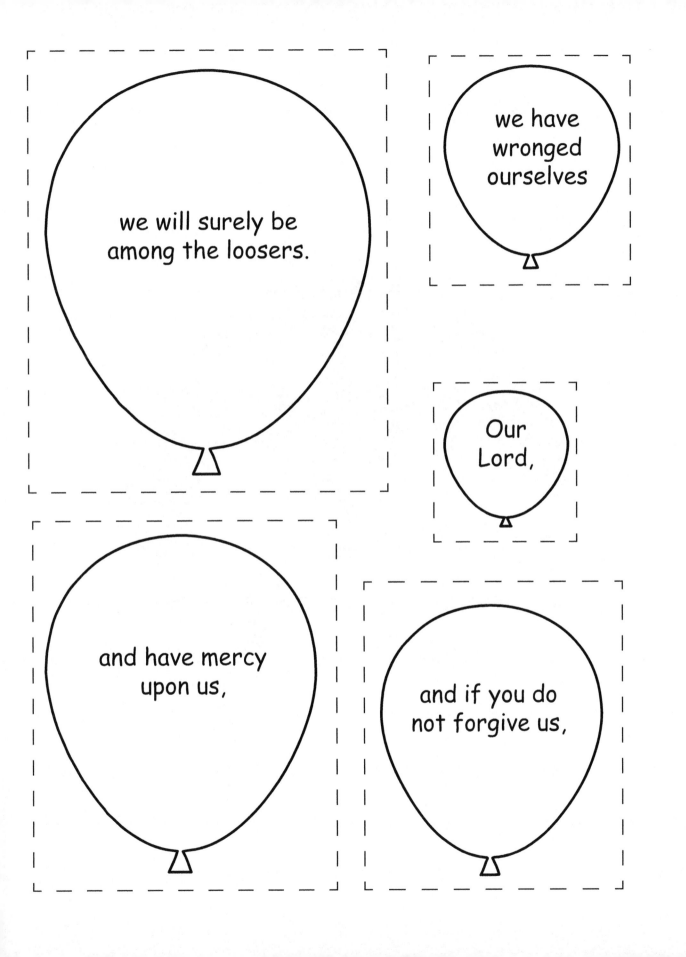

Stories of the Prophets

قصص الأنبياء

عليه السلام

Glorious
Guides

Colour me in

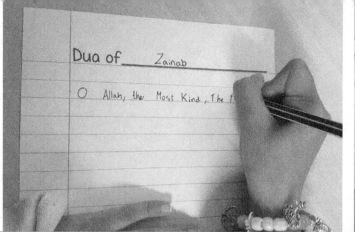
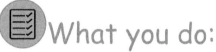

My Dua (Prayer)

Let us practice doing Istighfar a bit more so that we may develop it into a habit.

What you need:
–Activity Sheet
–Pen / Pencil

What you do:
–Write your name on blank space at the top.
–Now make your own dua for Istighfar and write it down.
(You can write in Arabic, English or any other language. Allah SWT can understand all languages and read all hand-writing. He even knows the thoughts that are in your mind!)

Top Tip: Praise Allah SWT before asking. Just like you praise your mum (You are the bestest mum in the whole wide world!) before asking for more chocolate cake!

Note for grown-ups: Remind and encourage children to do Istighfar frequently. They can use the Dua of Prophet Adam AS and also make up their own dua in their own language. Their own Dua will be more personal to them and mentioning their mistakes to Allah SWT will give them inner peace. It will provide perspective and drive them to stay away from the tricks of Shaytan in future.

Dua of _____

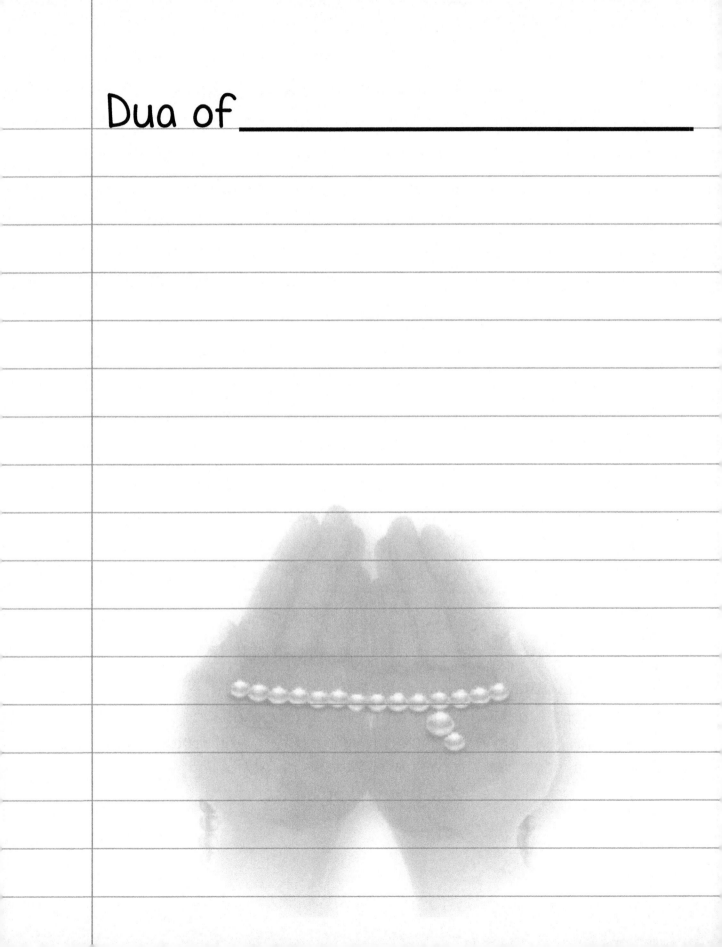

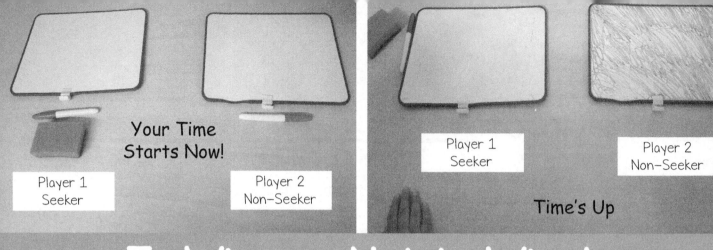

Your Time
Starts Now!

Player 1
Seeker

Player 2
Non-Seeker

Player 1
Seeker

Player 2
Non-Seeker

Time's Up

To Wipe or Not to Wipe!

It's time for some messy fun. This game is for 2 players but can be easily adapted for 2 teams.

 ## What you need:

–Two whiteboards
–Two whiteboard markers
–A whiteboard eraser/ sponge/ cloth etc to clean the whiteboards.
–Timer/ stop watch/ watch.
–A grown-up to act as the Game Moderator (GM).

 ## Game Set-up:

–Player 1 is the "Seeker" and gets One whiteboard, one whiteboard marker and one whiteboard eraser.
–Player 2 is the "Non-seeker" and gets one whiteboard and one whiteboard marker (no eraser).

 ## What you do:

–The GM says "Your time starts now!" and starts the timer. (Recommended time 2 minutes).
–Both players start scribbling on their whiteboards.
–The GM instructs the "Seeker" to wipe his/her whiteboard about every 30 seconds, while the "Non-seeker" keeps on scribbling.
–The GM says "Time's Up" at the end of allotted time.

—Now both players stop scribbling and show their whiteboards. (The whiteboard of the "Non-seeker" will be heavily marked, while the whiteboard of the "Seeker" will either be clean or minimally marked.)
—The GM now asks both players to explain why one whiteboard is dirtier / more marked than the other? The explanation should be linked to the concept of Istighfar.

Note for grown-ups: This activity is designed to help teach the significance and power of Istighfar. Listen to the children's answers at the end of the game and help them link it to the concept of Istighfar. Istighfar wipes away our mistakes and bad deeds just like the eraser has wiped away all the marks from the whiteboard.

Boost the discussion depending on the age of your child and level of understanding. Here are some ideas that you might find useful with older kids.

Concept of the "Book of Deeds" (Nama-e-Amaal): Just like the marker has left a mark on the white board, all our actions are also recorded in our "Book of Deeds".

Concept of "On-going Charity" (Sadaqah Jariyah): If the time runs out and Player 1's (Seeker) whiteboard is not entirely clean. You can use this opportunity to explain that he/ she is not allowed to use eraser after the time of the game has finished. In the same way, Istighfar is only accepted till your time in this world ends. After it no Istighfar or good deeds are possible except from the Sadqah Jariyah.

Also note that if you do not have a whiteboard then you can make your own by laminating a sheet of white paper, or use any suitable replacement e.g. chalkboard and chalk.

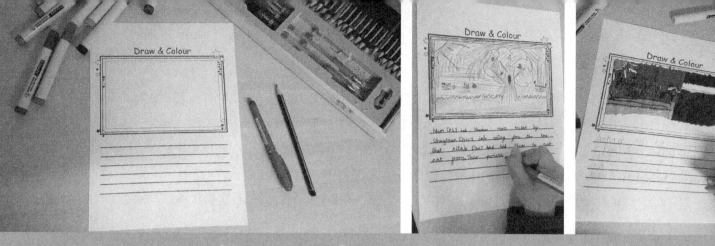

Draw & Colour

Which part of the story did you like best? Draw it using your own imagination.

 What you need:

–Activity Sheet
–Colouring pens
–Pen/ Pencil

 What you do:

–Draw a picture about the story of Prophet Adam AS,
–Now write a sentence about the picture you have drawn, using your own words.

👍 **Top Tip:** We do not draw the faces of Prophets. This is to show them respect.

Draw & Colour

Cut & Paste

Another chance to use scissors and glue!

 ## What you need:
–Activity Sheet.
–Child–safe scissors.
–Blank sheet of paper.
–Glue.
–Pencil/pen.

 ## What you do:
–Take the Activity sheet and cut along the dotted lines.
–Now take a blank sheet of paper and arrange all the pictures on it, in the correct story order.
–When you are happy with your arrangement, glue them down.
–Now take a pencil/pen and draw arrows to show the flow of the story to complete your Story Map.

Note for grown-ups: Help your child re-tell the story using the Story Map.

Stories of the Prophets

قصص الأنبياء

عليه السلام

Glorious
Guides

Word Jumble

Can you unscramble these jumbled up words?

MDAA   _____ _____ _____ _____

RREAOCT   _____ _____ _____ _____ _____ _____ _____

SANLEG   _____ _____ _____ _____ _____ _____

INJN   _____ _____ _____ _____

YOBE   _____ _____ _____ _____

LAYC   _____ _____ _____ _____

DOURP   _____ _____ _____ _____ _____

VERFIGO   _____ _____ _____ _____ _____ _____ _____

REMYC   _____ _____ _____ _____ _____

KICRT   _____ _____ _____ _____ _____

Break the Code

Write the first letter of each image on the line above it to complete the sentences.

Allah SWT made the Angels from

___ ___ ___ ___ ___

Allah SWT made the Jinns from

___ ___ ___ ___

Allah SWT made the Human from

___ ___ ___ ___

A Heavenly Sight

Flex your fingers and let your imagination run wild.

 ## What you need:
–Activity Sheet
–Colouring pens
–Craft & Decoration supplies
(e.g. sequins, pom poms, glitter, cupcake cases, confetti.)
–Glue

What you do:
–Decorate the tree to make it look like it's from paradise. Make it more beautiful than any tree in this world!
–Draw its background (if you like). It can have flowers, flowing streams or maybe even a few birds.

👍 **Top Tip:** It really does not matter how or what you use to decorate this tree, as long as you use your imagination.

*Disclaimer: Though we have been given some information about Paradise in the Qur'an but still it is not possible for the human mind to comprehend its beauty. The image of Paradise we can visualise is way inferior to its actual glory due to our limited knowledge and imagination.

A Heavenly Sight

English to Arabic

Join the English phrases to their Arabic counterparts

Ka'aba   مَلَآئِكَة

Bow down   جَنَّة

Adam AS   الْخَالِقُ

Angels   مُعْجِزَة

Deputy   خَلِيفَة

Creator   أَدَمُّ

Paradise   الكَعْبَة

Miracle   سَجْدَة

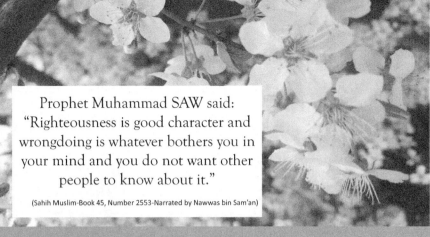

Prophet Muhammad SAW said:
"Righteousness is good character and wrongdoing is whatever bothers you in your mind and you do not want other people to know about it."

(Sahih Muslim-Book 45, Number 2553-Narrated by Nawwas bin Sam'an)

Making Good Choices

Every day we need to make choices. When to get out of bed in the morning, which clothes to wear, which words to use when talking and so many more in a single day. At times, making a choice can be tricky.

We need to learn to make good choices so we can stay safe, learn and have fun and also to ensure that others around us stay safe and happy.

Learning the ways of Allah SWT's Prophets, will help us to make good choices.

Note for grown-ups: Read the above text with your children and help them understand the concept of choices. Try to practice this concept in everyday life.
We have included some activities and game ideas to help understand and practice this concept.
Do give them a go.

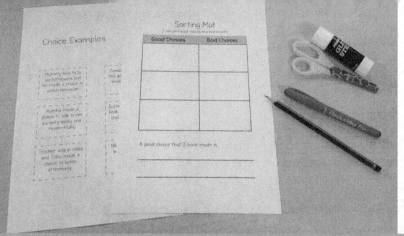

Good Choice, Bad Choice

Snip, snip. Yes, it's time to cut with scissors again.

 ## What you need:

−'Choice Examples' and 'Sorting Mat' Activity Sheets
−Child safe scissors.
−Glue
−Pencil/ pen.

 ## What you do:

−Take the 'Choice Examples' Activity Sheet and cut along the dotted lines.
−Then take the 'Sorting Mat' Activity Sheet and stick each 'Choice Example' in the correct column.
−Now take your pencil/pen and write down a good choice that you have made.

Note for grown-ups: This activity is a good way of initiating thoughts and develop understanding about choices. Everyday examples reinforce the fact that we need to make choices on daily basis.

Choice Examples

Mummy told Ali to do homework but he made a choice to watch television.

Zainab saw a cat in the garden and she made a choice to kick it.

Ayesha made a choice to talk to her parents nicely and respectfully.

Qasim was reading a book and he made a choice to rip out a page.

Talha made a choice to listen attentively in class.

Hiba made a choice to share her toys with her friends.

Stories of the Prophets

قصص الأنبياء

عليه السلام

Glorious
Guides

Sorting Mat

I can sort good choices and bad choices

Good Choices	Bad Choices

A good choice that I have made is

_____

_____

Tap a Choice

No time to sit around, put your running shoes on.

 ## What you need:

—A grown–up to act as the Game Moderator (GM).

—Two "Choice Cards"
(You can draw your own or use the ones given).

—One "Game Spot".
(This is the spot where the player will sit. It can be a cushion or just a designated place at one end of the room.)

—"Choice Examples" to be read out by the GM.

—Counters (You can use your own or colour and cut out the ones provided)

 ## Game set-up:

—The GM puts the two 'Choice Cards' at either end of the room, making sure they are well apart and that the player can see them from the 'Game Spot'.

—The GM asks the player to show their 'good sitting' and 'good listening' behaviour on the 'Game Spot'.

What you do:

−The GM reads out one 'Choice Example'.
−The GM gives the player a moment to think and then says 'Tap a Choice' out loud.
−The player has to decide whether that 'Choice Example' is a good or bad choice. Then run to the relevant 'Choice Card' and tap it.
−The GM notes it and asks player to come back to the 'Game Spot'.
−If the answer is correct then the player gets one counter.
−The GM reads the next 'Choice Example' and so on.

Note for grown-ups: This game is more suitable for younger children who love to run around.

The instructions provided are for one player but the game can be easily adapted for two or more players.

You can always make up your own 'Choice Examples' that are more relevant to your Child's understanding, day−to−day activities or any particular area of behaviour you want to target (Classroom behaviour, sibling rivalry etc.).

Show excitement yourself, give lots of targeted praise and maybe a little prize in the end.

Choice Examples

—Ali made a lot of noise in class.

—Sadia held her mummy's hand while crossing the road.

—Amna sat on the slide and did not let other children have a turn.

—Zainab helped her baby brother climb down the bed safely.

—Yusuf gave his seat in the bus to an elderly man.

—Ibrahim used kind words and showed good manners at lunch time.

—Ahmed played his video game all day and missed all his prayers (Salah).

—Zoya sat and watched TV while her mum set the table for dinner.

—Musa vacuumed the house on the weekend.

—Shiza held the door open for an elderly lady to pass through.

—Omar snatched the toy car from his baby brother and made him cry.

—Fatima talked with her mouth full of food.

Choice Cards

Good Choice

Bad Choice

Stories of the Prophets
قصص الأنبياء
عليه السلام
Glorious Guides

Counters

Stories of the Prophets

قصص الأنبياء

عليه السلام

Glorious
Guides

Colour me in

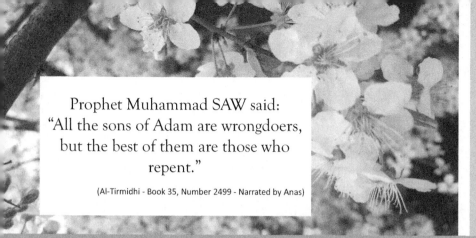

Prophet Muhammad SAW said:
"All the sons of Adam are wrongdoers, but the best of them are those who repent."

(Al-Tirmidhi - Book 35, Number 2499 - Narrated by Anas)

Be Brave, Say Sorry

We all make mistakes, intentionally or unintentionally and we can hurt other people with our actions and behaviours. None of us is perfect.

So we all need to learn how to apologise.

It isn't always easy to apologise, but it's the most effective way to bring back the trust and balance in a relationship.

A sincere apology shows that you're taking responsibility for your actions. You will feel a sense of relief when you come clean about your actions.

Saying sorry for your mistakes makes the other person happy, makes Allah SWT happy, and most of all, makes YOU happy. Try it. You'll be amazed at how good it feels.

The Golden Rule of F.S.A.N

F is for "Feel Sorry":
Firstly, we should admit our mistake to ourselves, truly regret it and feel bad for doing it.

S is for "Say Sorry":
Then we should use words to apologise and seek forgiveness for our bad action(s). Our words need to sound sincere, that we really mean them.

A is for "Act Sorry":
This is the action part. We should immediately stop doing the bad action. Then we should try to perform an additional good action, to compensate for the bad action which we have done.

N is for "Not Again":
We should try our best to never make the same mistake again.

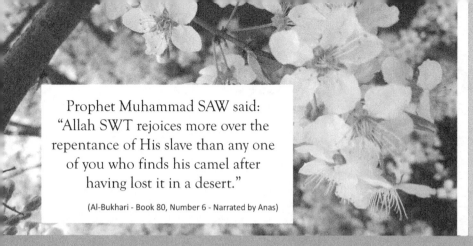

> Prophet Muhammad SAW said:
> "Allah SWT rejoices more over the repentance of His slave than any one of you who finds his camel after having lost it in a desert."
>
> (Al-Bukhari - Book 80, Number 6 - Narrated by Anas)

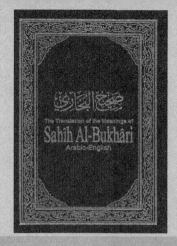

Saying Sorry to Allah SWT

Saying sorry is also known as repentance, Tauba and Istighfar. If we ever disobey Allah SWT then we should repent and seek Allah SWT's forgiveness.

F.S.A.N Way of Sorry

F Feel Sorry	Truly regret the disobedience. Allah SWT knows what is in your heart and all your feelings.
S Say Sorry	Do Istighfar. Do not delay it.
A Act Sorry	Stop the bad deed immediately and follow it by good deeds.
N Never Again	Make a sincere intention to not go back to the bad deed. Never, ever!

Top Tip: It does not matter if you have to repeat this process ten times, a hundred times or an infinite number of times. Allah SWT will always accept it. In fact, it makes Allah SWT extremely happy when someone repents and seeks His forgiveness.

My name is Saba

My mistake is that I was singing loudly at the same time as the Azan was being called.

F.S.A.N Way of Sorry

 **F** Feel Sorry	I realised that what I did was very disrespectful and I felt very ashamed.
 **S** Say Sorry	I said "Astagh firullah, Allah Tallah please forgive my mistake. I was being very naughty"
 **A** Act Sorry	I stopped singing. Sat down and listened to the rest of Azan respectfully. I laid down the prayer mat for daddy.
 **N** Never Again	Now I don't make any noise at Azan time. I listen to it quietly and respectfully.

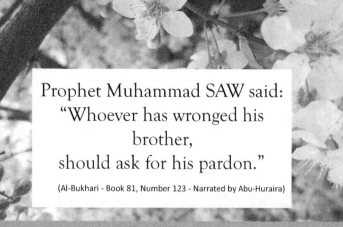

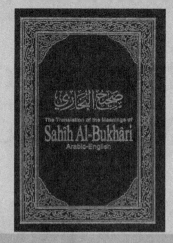

Prophet Muhammad SAW said:
"Whoever has wronged his brother,
should ask for his pardon."

(Al-Bukhari - Book 81, Number 123 - Narrated by Abu-Huraira)

Saying Sorry to People

If we ever do something bad to a person, we should always say sorry.

F.S.A.N. Way of Sorry

F Feel Sorry	Admit responsibility for our actions or behaviour. Regret doing it and feel guilty.
S Say Sorry	Yup say the magic word "Sorry". Apologise as soon as you can and make sure you sound sincere.
A Act Sorry	Take action to make the situation right. Try to fix what went wrong and then try to do something nice in addition to it.
N Never Again	Your last step is to explain that you won't repeat the action or behaviour. This helps to rebuild trust and repair the relationship.

👍 **Top Tip:** Make sure that you honour this commitment in the days or weeks to come. If you promise to change your behaviour, but don't follow through, others will question your reputation and your trustworthiness.

People can not forgive infinite number of times like Allah SWT.

41

My name is Ahmed

My mistake is that Broke mum's tea cup because I was watching TV and not looking where I was going.

F.S.A.N. Way of Sorry

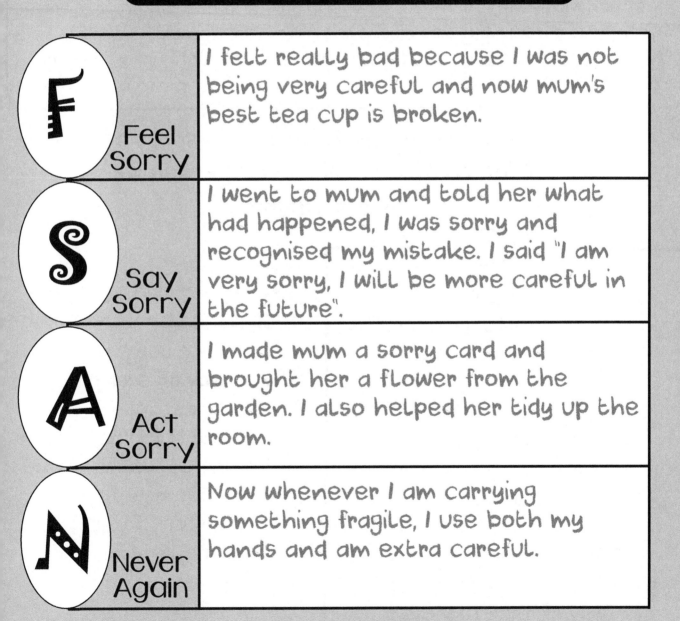

F Feel Sorry	I felt really bad because I was not being very careful and now mum's best tea cup is broken.
S Say Sorry	I went to mum and told her what had happened, I was sorry and recognised my mistake. I said "I am very sorry, I will be more careful in the future".
A Act Sorry	I made mum a sorry card and brought her a flower from the garden. I also helped her tidy up the room.
N Never Again	Now whenever I am carrying something fragile, I use both my hands and am extra careful.

Sometimes the mistakes we make
not only result in Allah SWT's disobedience
but also effect people. For example:

Being disrespectful towards your parents

Allah SWT has ordered us to be obedient to our parents and be at our best behaviour with them. So, by being rude to them, we are not only hurting our parents but also disobeying Allah SWT's order.
Backbiting, hitting siblings and stealing are also acts that hurt people and make Allah SWT unhappy.

In such cases we have to say sorry to
Allah SWT as well as the person we
have wronged.

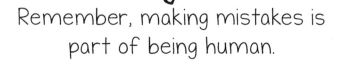

Remember, making mistakes is part of being human.

Being stubborn, not admitting your mistake, and showing arrogance is the way of Shaytaan.

Whereas admitting your mistake and saying sorry is the way of the Prophets.

 Note for grown-ups:
Help children use **'F.S.A.N. way of sorry'** Activity Sheet to understand and practice apologising, as well as to demonstrate how they have said sorry for a mistake they had made.

My name is

My mistake is that

F.S.A.N. Way of Sorry

F Feel Sorry	
S Say Sorry	
A Act Sorry	
N Never Again	

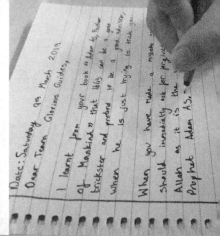

Write to Us

Write a letter to the team at 'Glorious Guides', telling us:

–Lessons you have learnt, or

–Good habits that you have adopted, or

–any other thoughts that came to your mind after reading the story of Prophet Adam AS.

We would love to hear from you. Send it to us via our website:
www.lastinglegacy.club

Note for grown-ups: Assist children to reflect on the story of Prophet Adam AS and develop understanding of the concepts and lessons relayed through the story.

A few examples of lessons learnt can be:

–Disobeying Allah SWT and being stubborn about it is the way of Shaytaan.

–Never think that you are superior to anyone else.

–Repenting and asking for forgiveness are from the way of the Prophets. They make Allah SWT happy and He not only forgives us but also showers us with blessings and rewards.

–Shaytaan can come to trick us by pretending to be a well–wisher and good advisor. So if we are not very vigilant, we can easily fall for his tricks. We should make a habit of asking Allah SWT to protect us from Shaytaan and his tricks.

Date

Dear Team Glorious Guides,

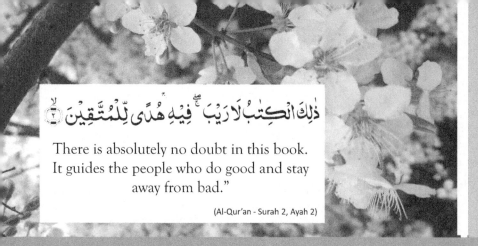

ذَٰلِكَ ٱلْكِتَٰبُ لَا رَيْبَ ۛ فِيهِ ۛ هُدًى لِّلْمُتَّقِينَ ٢

There is absolutely no doubt in this book.
It guides the people who do good and stay
away from bad."

(Al-Qur'an - Surah 2, Ayah 2)

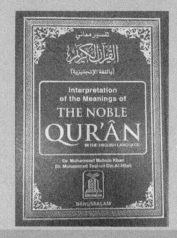

Look Around You

The Qur'an is a Book of
Guidance for all people,
for all time.

Allah SWT has mentioned the story of Prophet Adam AS in the Qur'an, so the message and guidance in this story has to be relevant to us and the world around us.

Let's see how we can apply our understanding of the story of Prophet Adam AS to some real-world examples.

Example 1: Shutting Door

Musa was leaving the house. He came through the door and shut it without looking. A scream made him look back and he realised that his little sister was behind him and he had shut the door on her hand. She was crying with pain.

Musa realised his mistake: he had not been careful enough and had hurt his little sister by mistake. He felt really sorry, apologised to his sister, checked for any possible injury, comforted her and held her hand until she felt better.

Question: How would you describe Musa's behaviour, in the light of the story of Prophet Adam AS?

Question: Was Musa following the way of Prophet Adam AS or the way of Shaytan? Why do you think so?

Note for grown-ups: Help the child link this example to the story of Prophet Adam AS. The character in this example did not show arrogance like Shaytan. He was humble and regretted his mistake, just like Prophet Adam AS.

He apologised and tried to make amends.

Assist your child to generalise the concepts of realising mistakes, apologising and making amends.

Example 2: Richie Rich

Salma was a very rich lady. One day she took Sana, her five-year-old daughter, to a park.

Sana met a lovely little girl whose appearance was a bit shabby, and started to play with her.

When Salma saw this, she quickly grabbed Sana's hand and took her away, saying that Sana is from a richer, better family and should not play with such poor, dirty and worthless kids.

Question: How would you describe Salma's behaviour, in light of the story of Prophet Adam AS?

Question: Was Salma following the way of Prophet Adam AS or the way of Shaytan? Why do you think so?

Note for grown-ups: Help the child link this example to the story of Prophet Adam AS. The character Salma, in this example, expressed her feelings of superiority, just like Shaytan thought he was superior to Prophet Adam AS.

Assist your child to generalise the concept of equality of humankind. All humans are created equal. No human is superior to another on basis of skin colour, wealth or family. It is only our good deeds that increase our ranks.

On Point

A show where kids talk and grown-ups listen!

Talk Show

Hold your own TV talk show on the hot topic:

> "Prophet Adam AS and Azazeel both disobeyed Allah SWT's command. But Adam AS was honoured with Prophethood while Azazeel was proclaimed to be Iblees (dishonoured). Why such a contrast? "

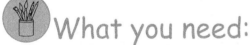

What you need:
- 'Talk Show' host (The grown-up)
- Guest Analyst (The child)
- Props (if you like) e.g. pretend microphone

What you do:
- Host starts the show, welcomes and introduces the guest analyst. Introduces the topic and starts the talk.
- Discuss the topic and don't forget to go for commercial breaks!
- The host thanks the analyst and sums up the discussion.

Note for grown-ups:
Check for kid's understanding by looking out for concepts like Azazeel disobeying knowingly and out of pride and arrogance but Prophet Adam AS disobeying by mistake, as a result of trickery. Also, Azazeel did not repent; on the contrary he was stubborn, while Prophet Adam AS repented immediately and copiously and asked for forgiveness. Any other answers the kids can come up with are also fine, as long as they can support their argument with reasons.

Thinking Hats on

This activity is ideally for two or more players but one player can also complete it.

What you need:
–One big sheet of paper
–Sticky notes
–Pen/ pencil

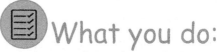

What you do:
– Write "Prophet Adam AS" on the big sheet of paper and put it in front of the players.

–Each player gets a pen and sticky notes. He/she thinks of words or phrases that describe Prophet Adam AS and writes them on sticky notes.

–When done, the players stick the sticky notes on the big sheet of paper one-by-one.

Note for grown-ups: This activity helps kids think more profoundly about the character traits of Propet Adam AS, which will ultimately help them to figure out the deeper meaning of the story. Character traits can be visual descriptions, actions, conversations, thoughts etc. (Examples might include: human, created, prophet, repented, sent from Paradise to Earth, got tricked, builder of the Ka'bah, builder of Al-Aqsa, Father of Humankind etc.)

Points to Ponder

Here are a couple of points for you to think about.

The Great Debate

"Are pranks just light-hearted and funny jokes, to be enjoyed by all? Or are they tricks and the way of Iblees?"

What do you think?
Discuss with a grown-up or write your answer, giving all the reasons and arguments you can think of.

Why is that so!

Prophet Adam AS included in his dua the words 'Zalamna anfusana' which mean 'we have wronged ourselves'.
What did Prophet Adam AS mean by this part of the Dua? How is it that by doing bad deeds we are actually doing wrong to our own selves?

Have a think.
You can always go to a grown-up for help, or look up the tafseer or Google it.

Answers

Answers of the questions in story book of Prophet Adam AS:

Answer 1: C. Without the help of anyone.
Answer 2: A. Light
Answer 3: B. Devils.
Answer 4: B. An appointee who can exercise some of the power of its superior.
Answer 5: A. Bow down to Prophet Adam AS.
Answer 6: C. Because he was too proud and thought he was better than Prophet Adam AS.
Answer 7: A. Knowledge of names of things.
Answer 8: B. A tree in paradise.
Answer 9: A. He tricked Prophet Adam AS into eating fruit of the forbidden tree.
Answer 10: A. Iblees wanted Allah SWT to be angry at Prophet Adam AS.

English to Arabic:

Ka'aba   الكَعْبَة
Bow down   سَجْدَة
Adam AS   أدَمٌ
Angels   مَلَآئِكَة
Deputy   خَلِيفَة

Creator   الْخَالِقُ
Paradise   جَنَّة
Miracle   مُعْجِزَة

Break the Code:

—Allah SWT made the Angels from LIGHT
—Allah SWT made the Jinns from FIRE
—Allah SWT made the Human from CLAY

Word Jumble:

MDAA = ADAM
RREAOCT = CREATOR
SANLEG = ANGELS
INJN = JINN
YOBE = OBEY
LAYC = CLAY
DOURP – PROUD
VERFIGO = FORGIVE

Certificate

Date

_____

Congratulations to

_____

(Write your name here)

For completing the activities

Excellent Work!

You are a Lasting Legacy Super Star

Printed in Great Britain
by Amazon